When·God·Began·in·the·Middle

Joseph J. Juknialis

I began loved,
in the middle of their lives —

To My Parents

Copyright © 1982 by Resource Publications, Inc.
P. O. Box 444, Saratoga, CA 95071. All rights reserved.
Printed and bound in the United States of America 4 3 2 1.

Acknowledgements:
Scripture texts used in "Traces of Stars" are taken from the New American
Bible, copyright © 1970, by the Confraternity of Christian Doctrine,
Washington, D.C., are used by permission of copyright owner. All rights
reserved.
Cover design, book design, and illustrations by Rev. Tom Fait.

Library of Congress Catalog No. 81-52597
ISBN 0-89390-027-3

CONTENTS

PREFACE

The God in whom we believe
is a God who comes into our lives
from beginning to end.

He comes as life unfolds,
threading a seam between winter and spring.

He is present in moments of death,
harvesting the fruits of our autumns.

But most frequently he comes into the middle of life,
in the summer of our days.

He comes into the midst of success and of failure,
into fear as well as into comfort.

He makes himself known in moments of grace
and in moments of sin,
in love
and in loneliness.

It is in the middle of our lives
that we come to realize what faith means
and what it demands.

It is in the middle of our lives
that love is redefined,
that the seeds of wisdom are sown,
that we begin to surrender control over our lives
to a force greater than ourselves.

Those who have journeyed the middle of life
carry with them
forever
the memories of times
WHEN GOD BEGAN IN THE MIDDLE.

In the beginning, When God Began in the Middle

Twixt
Spring
And
Autumn

A Story for Summer

On the eighth day of creation,
the morning following the day of rest,
God was awakened by a boisterous pounding on his door.
From his sky blue window he caught a glimpse of his visitors —
each of the four seasons,
Winter and Spring, Autumn and Summer.
"We need to know who will come first
and who will be greatest," was their demand.
And so it was, no sooner had God finished his creation
than there began to be disagreements.
It was on that day
that God called into being his first cosmic hearing.

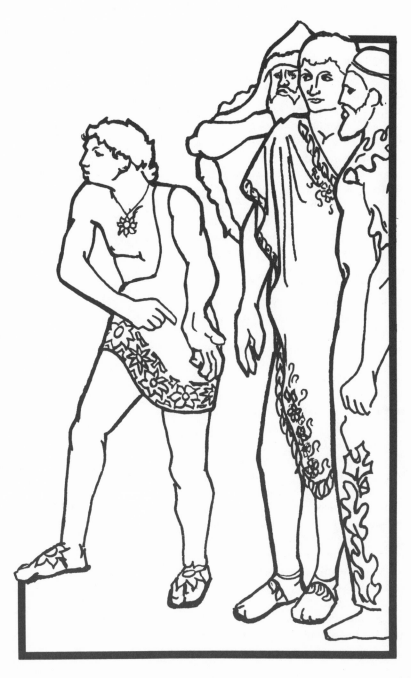

11

He spoke to them in this way:
"All of you are a part of my creation
and so you are all equally a portion of my love.
I cannot appoint one of you to be first
nor can I establish one as greatest,
but each of you I will gift so each of you may be unique —
each loved in your own way."

Winter was the first to come forth.
"To you I give the gift of anticipation and preparation.
Your task will be to prepare for new life.
You shall set the patterns for colors and hues.
You shall be the one to instill within the oak
the ability to be strong
and within the rose
its breathtaking delicacy.
You shall give form and shape
even before it is.
You shall be the father and mother of what will be."
And it was early dawn,
the eighth day,
and Winter went away — very happy.
And God saw that it as good.

Next he called forth Spring.
"To you I give the gift of new life.
You shall give innocence to my creation
and be blest with hope for the new born.
With tenderness you will give care,
and nurture weakness unfolding into strength.
You will know the joy of discovery
and the excitement of new treasures previously unknown.
You shall be the child of all that will be."
And it was morning,
the eighth day,
and Spring went away — very happy.
And God saw that it was good.

It came time then for the third season,
Autumn,
to receive its gift.
"Yours will be the gift of death —
not a death shrouded in pain and sadness,
rather, it shall be the joy
of seeing the fulfillment of what has gone before.
You will know the goodness of life richly lived.
You will taste the sweetness of life harvested and shared."
And it was twilight,
the eighth day,
and Autumn went away — very happy.
And God saw that it was good.

Finally, it was Summer's turn to come forth
and receive its gift.
And then it was that God realized
he had no gift for Summer.
To Winter he had given the ability to prepare and to form.
To Spring it had been new life.
And to Autumn it had been life
harvested in the fruitfulness of death.
What then remained for Summer?

While no one spoke,
Summer realized what was happening —
there was no gift.

Suddenly,
lest he be trapped by his own generosity,
God smiled and said,
"Fear not.
To you I will give the gift of growth.
You shall live twixt
Spring
and
Autumn.
You shall inherit the gift of Spring

as well as touch the gift of Autumn.
You,
with your gift of growth,
shall be the bridge between
life and death."

But Summer was not happy.
"I do not wish to tell you how to run your world,
O God,
nor do I wish to seem ungrateful,"
said Summer,
"but, you see,
growth is so terribly painful
and negligibly slow
that while you have indeed blest me,
I fear I shall never know or experience it."
How true and how wise,
thought God.
He paused —
and thought even more.
"You are quite right, Summer.
I have blest you,
but your gift remains hidden.
And so you I will bless twice.
You shall keep your gift twixt
Spring
and
Autumn,
but in addition,
I will give to you the gift of
People.

People who are happy
and share life with their families.
People who will picnic on my hillsides
and splash in my streams.
People who will rejoice in my gift of creation
and sing praise in life lived deeply.

14

And thus it was that Summer was blest twice over
when God
gave to Summer
the gift of
People.

And it was noon.
Winter and Spring and Autumn had all gone away —
one day to return.
But Summer stayed —
very happy,
knowing that it had been specially blest by God.

And God smiled and saw that it was good.

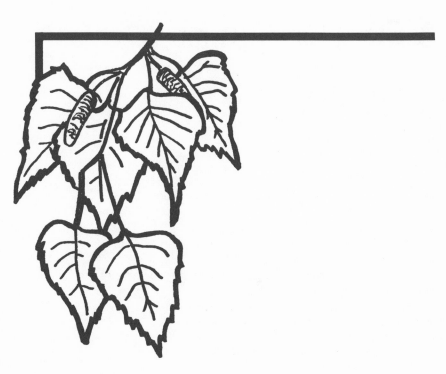

The
Memory
Trees

A Story for Autumn

As God's creation began to unfold and take shape,
so did the seasons of time,
each gifted by God in its own manner.
To Winter God had given the gift of preparation for life,
the ability to give form to what would be.
Spring had been given the gift of birth and the newness of life.
Summer had been gifted with growth,
and Autumn had received the gift of bearing fruit.
However, Summer had been twice blessed —
or so the story has been told —
and had received the gift of people as well.

17

Such a blessing, doubly offered,
was indeed a delight as long as Summer colored the days.
But as the days of Summer, yet to be shared, grew fewer,
and as Autumn's excitement grew
in anticipation of its opportunity to reign,
grumblings began to be heard among the people.
If it was true, and indeed it seemed that it was,
that people had been made for Summer
and gifted to Summer,
then it was only natural for them to leave when Summer left.
They belonged to Summer in their hearts
and in their spirits.

Waiting close by to make its appearance,
it was not unusual that Autumn caught word
of the intended desertion.
With only a week remaining until Summer's days would be spent,
Autumn concluded that the only one who could resolve the confusion
was the one who created the situation in the beginning.
Autumn knocked on God's door.

Indeed, God was taken aback by Autumn's mournful presence.
"You have not yet reigned even once,"
wondered God aloud.
"Is it possible that dissatisfaction has already come about?"

"Allow me to explain, O God,"pleaded Autumn.
"It was indeed a wise decision when,
on the eighth day of creation,
you blessed Summer twice over with the gift of people.
They have given new meaning to all that is
and have brought joy to all of your creation."

"Then what seems to be the problem?" asked God.
"It is this," replied Autumn.
"When you gave them as a gift to Summer,
it seems that they became a part of Summer.
It seems that their thoughts and dreams,

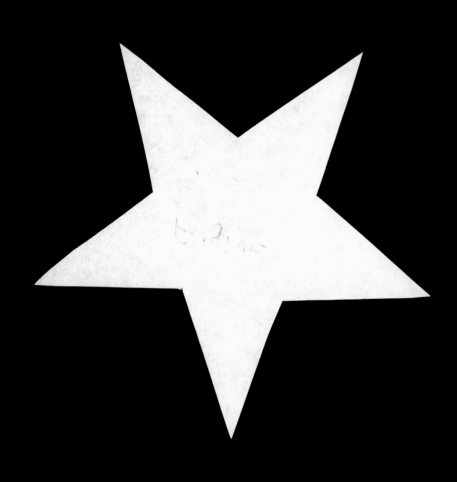

their hopes and futures
all so totally reflect Summer
that now as Summer prepares to leave,
so too do the people intend to leave with Summer.
I realize, my God, that they are Summer's gift,
yet if they leave with Summer
then I fear that the fruit born by me will never be shared.
I ask you, O God,
what good is it to have been gifted with the bearing of fruit
if that fruit is never to be shared?"

"What you are asking of me then, Autumn,
is to bless you with people as well —
just as I did Summer.
Is that not correct?" asked God.

"If that seems best to you, O God, I would be most happy.
However, might I suggest that such is not necessary.
To continue to bless each season anew would be most generous,
yet it would seem that all you need do
is to make it known that the people of Summer
are truly the people af all seasons, of all times and all ages.
It would be much more simple
and less troublesome
than beginning each season with new people."

"There is much thought in your suggestion," replied God.
"I will consider what you ask."

God did consider Autumn's request
and recognized the wisdom with which it was made.
Thus on the next day God called Summer to his kingdom hall.
He explained the request put forth by Autumn
and instructed Summer to inform the people of his decision
that they remain for all seasons.
He assured Summer
that people would always be born
with the spirit of Summer in their hearts,

yet what was given to one season
must now be shared with all seasons.

Word spread quickly among the people
and, as is usually the case, first reactions were overreactions.
There were those who suggested mutiny against God
but then remembered the plight of the angels.
Others thought of quietly slipping away with Summer
— hopefully unnoticed,
but they recalled how all of God's creation revealed his presence
and thus there would be no escaping.
Others thought of banding together and refusing Autumn entrance
but then also realized
how the rhythm at the center of all creation can never be stopped.
In the end, they realized that Summer had to leave
and that they would have to learn how to live with Autumn.
It was in the wisdom of this final realization
that their plan evolved.
Early on the last day of Summer,
those appointed for the task
began the gathering of memories.
It had been decided
that if all of the people had to remain for all the seasons,
then at least they would hold on to their memories of Summer
so that the spirit of Summer living in their hearts
might find strength.
Those gathering memories went to every person in the land,
to every mother and father and child,
to every neighbor and every stranger.
Each was asked to form their memory with care
and gently place it in the basket
used to gather the memories.

As the last day of Summer neared its end,
the baskets gradually began to fill with all kinds of memories.
There were memories of the warm sun
and the delight it offered.
There were memories of love

shared at picnics and family gatherings.
There were memories of simple fun,
of swimming in streams
and running through fields
and climbing broad-branched trees.
There were memories of new friendships
and memories of the earth and its flowering hues.
Newborn memories of every kind
filled the baskets to overflowing.
As Summer departed with the final rays of the setting sun,
both the people who remained
and Summer who took leave
knew that their friendship would last.
There was sadness in those final moments,
but it was touched with the joyful hope
of once again meeting.

After Summer had left
and all the people had returned to their homes,
those who had gathered the memories met to sort them out
so that they might be stored for future needs.
Yet it had grown late
and their eyes were heavy from their day long task.
It had grown dark with the setting sun,
and the Autumn moon had not yet made herself known
for she was a blessing yet to be discovered.
Since the darkness of the night
prevented the gatherers from sorting the memories
and since the memories themselves were yet moist
in their recently formed existence,
those who had gathered the memories
decided to hang them in the branches of the trees
that they might dry during the night.
In that darkness
they swiftly draped the trees with their newly gathered memories,
randomly scattering the contents of their baskets
over the wooded land in which they lived.

When the task was completed
each went to his own home to find rest for his weary spirit.
The early morning was awakened
by shouts of surprise and excitement.
The people found their land lavishly alive
with the colors of their memories
scattered over the trees.
Golden yellow memories of the warm sun
hung in every tree.
Bold red memories of love shared at family picnics
pierced the hillsides.
Lively orange memories of shared fun,
memories of swimming and running and climbing
shouted life from every direction.
Autumn green memories of new friendships
were tucked in every valley,
and rusty colored memories of the good earth and her summer gifts
broke forth from every branch.
The memories of Summer had become a gift to Autumn
and the people who had been a gift to Summer
welcomed Autumn with gracious joy.

And so it is that every year
the story of Autumn is repeated.
On the last day of Summer
memories of that Summer are gathered
and hung on the trees to dry.
And each year the first Autumn morning comes
colored by Summer's memories.
There are some who out of eagerness
begin to share their memories days or even weeks before the last day.
And there are others whose colored memories are discovered a bit later
for they need to be convinced
that Summer has indeed left for one more year.
But for the most part, Autumn is able to be greeted with joy
because Summer has left behind
the marvelous memories of her warm and joy-filled days,
memories of yellow

and red
and orange
and green
and rusty brown.
Autumn is a time for remembering.

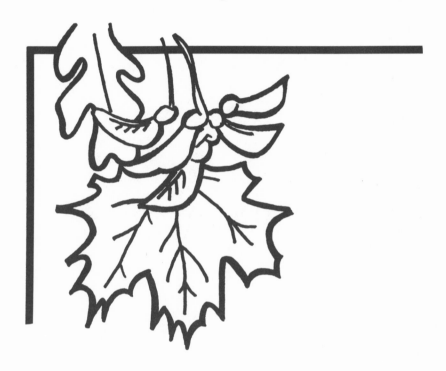

The
Night
Of
The
Great
Snow

A Story for Winter

In the beginning, God began in the middle.
That is to say,
though the seasons of God's unfolding love now begin with Winter,
God began in the middle with Summer.
Winter is the first of the Seasons,
for it is the season during which all of the patterns of what will be
are traced into the still spirits of his frozen creation.
It was to Summer, however,
that God had given the gift of people —
people who would share the warmth of his love
and delight in his creation.
Yet when the time came for Summer to leave

in order to make room for Autumn,
Summer's people were asked to remain with God's creation
and share in Autumn's harvest.
And because in their hearts they belonged to Summer,
the people carried with them brilliantly colored memories of Summer
which they hung in Autumn's trees —
red and gold and orange memories
of a warm and lasting friend.

In time, both the memories
and the colors of those memories began to fade.
Without the sun-filled memories
of summer picnics and the gurgling streams to bring warmth,
a new-born cold began to nest in Autumn's barren trees.
Chirping birds began to give way to whistling winds,
and occasional shivering gusts roamed as scavengers,
gathering leftover remnants of color and life.
The people grew fearful,
not understanding the cycle of life and death,
of birth and bearing fruit.

Thus the people made plans to confuse the winds
and to repel the cold.
It was their thinking that if they gathered in celebration
as they once did during the days of Summer,
perhaps in confusion
the cold and the wind would give way to warmth.
And so the people did gather with their friends.
They joined with one another
and shared Autumn's harvest gifts in Thanksgiving;
and for a time warmth did return.
It seemed as if the people of Summer had succeeded
in protecting themselves against Winter's advance.
For a few brief days it was once again Summer.
But the warmth of Thanksgiving was short lived.
Winter was too wise to be outsmarted
and too insistent to be denied its place in the cycle of seasons.
Thus is was that the people who had been born of Summer

26

and had journeyed through Autumn,
found themselves citizens of Winter.
Forgotten memories had made room for swirling winds.
In their struggle to survive,
Summer's people huddled together
so that they might bring warmth to one another.
At nighttime they gathered about fires
to tell stories of what once was —
corners of memories they had once lived.
There, with one another,
they shed tears of pain and fear and sadness.
With each story told and retold,
new tears flowed out into the darkness
and away from the warmth of their friendship.

In the morning the people awoke,
frightened and terrified,
for the earth had turned white,
snow-dressed in a gift they did not understand.
Unlike the sun, the snow was cold to the touch,
and they thought it to be evil.
Sliding and falling, they tried to run from it.
They sought to overcome it,
but even the sun had no power to conquer.
They were prisoners of Winter's snows.
Thus each night they gathered about their fires and told stories.
Each night they shed new tears;
and each morning they discovered that the snow had grown deeper.

The days soon began to gather themselves into weeks —
so many weeks that the calendar grew heavy.
Still the people did not understand;
still they gathered about their nighttime fires;
still Winter's snow remained.
Finally, the one among the people who had grown the wisest
called all of the people together.
All came;

all brought their own bits of remembered stories
and their own fires about which they gathered;
all journeyed, struggling through the very snow
they both feared and yet sought to understand.

That night the land burned with nighttime fires.
Everyone told their stories,
and everyone shed tears of frightened loneliness
for the Summer they once knew.
It was on that night that the people,
led by the wisest among them
came to a very important decision.
It was on that night,
the night of the Great Snow,
that the people of Summer decided to go to the Palace of Winter
in search of the one story
which would give meaning to all of the snow.
Those that had gathered about each of the storytelling fires
chose a representative to accompany the wise one
on the journey to Winter.
Together they would find strength
to overcome their fear of the snow,
and together they would possess the courage
to speak in the Palace of Winter.
They followed the wind and traveled with the cold
until they came upon Winter's crystal home.
Fearful of Winter and the welcome they expected to receive,
they walked through the palace gates,
climbed the steps carved in snow,
and found themselves standing before the one they had come to see.
Winter was waiting for them,
for his winds had brought the news
even as the journey was being planned.
To their surprise, Winter seemed kind and friendly,
not at all like his snow and his cold.

The wise one stepped forward, about to speak,

28

when Winter invited them to be seated.
Fire was brought in to warm them,
and sunlight glistened through the crystal windows.

"You have come," said Winter,
even before the wise one could speak,
"because you do not understand the snow.
You are fearful and confused,
and your days seem without meaning.
That is always how it is when one does not understand.
What you must know is that the snow has come from your tears.
In the darkness of the night, as you wept by your fires,
your tears flowed out into that darkness.
In the cold your tears turned frosted and white,
covering the entire land like the fear from which they flowed.
Yet because you did not understand,
your fear remained.
Thus it was on the night before you left,
the night when you gathered together about your fires,
that your tears flowed greatly, and it has come to be known as
the Night of the Great Snow."

The wise one and those who accompanied him sat in amazement
for it all seemed so clear and so simple.
No longer were they fearful, for now they understood.
The wise one then spoke,
"We are most grateful
that you have given us understanding and knowledge,
and we are certainly eager to return home
and share this good news with our families.
You have been most kind, for never again will we be fearful.
Never again will we need to shed tears.
Never again will there be a Night of the Great Snow.
For all ages you have freed us and our descendants
from the snows of Winter.
We are, indeed, most thankful."

They were about to rise and leave

when Winter spoke once more.
"I am afraid you have misunderstood,
or perhaps I need to explain more.
Please remain a bit longer.
It is true. You do understand,
and for you the snows of this season have ended.
But your spirits shall soon forget,
even though your minds will remember.
Come next Autumn, when Winter returns,
you will again cry tears of pain
and the snows shall return once more.
You see, there is a reason why it is so."

"You are a people who belong to Summer,
and because you do, you will always cling
to the memories of those warm, love-filled days.
But the cycle of the seasons must travel on.
Though Autumn allows you to cling to those memories,
there comes a time when you must let go of those memories,
in order to make room for new life and new memories.
If you are not willing to let go,
there can be no new life.
But the letting go shall always be painful and tear-filled.
What you must also know, however,
is that the melting snows,
once your tears of pain,
also give birth to the new life.
Without the melting snows there would be no new life
and no new memories.
And so it is that the tear-filled pain of letting go
is the very force which makes new life possible.
Without the pain,
there could be no new life when Summer returns.
That is how it must be.
That is why though your minds will remember,
each year your spirits will forget.
Each year you will need to travel deep into Winter
and discover anew the meaning of its snows —

its pains and fears
and the tears which are shed.
It is a sorrow which I bring, but also a gift."

A reverent, awesome silence clothed all who were present.
The wise one and those who accompanied him stood
and departed in wonder.
As they journeyed home they began to notice
that the snows were already beginning
to water the birth of new life,
and the wisdom they had come to know in the Palace of Winter
was already bearing the fruit of truth.
Once they arrived home,
they told all of their meeting with the season of Winter
and of the understanding they came to know.
In their joy,
the people celebrated the end of the snows.
And while their minds still remembered the truth they had been given,
already in their joy,
their spirits began to forget.

Once
In Every
Lifetime

A Story for Spring

There was a time, once, when stories were told in song
by troubadours who roamed from village to village.
With them they carried both lutes on which they sang their stories
and coats made of wool
which served as pillows on warm nights
and as blankets on cold nights.
No one, it seemed, ever knew whence they had come
or to what people they belonged.
Perhaps no one knew
because they simply were —
without past or future —
belonging to all people.

What follows is not a story told by a troubadour,
but rather a story about a troubadour,
a story remembered by the sun and told by the wind
to those who are able to believe with their hearts
rather than with their minds.

The fact that troubadours would wander through the land
was not of itself so unusual.
In fact, it seemed that each time of year
had its own minstrel of stories.
Summer days gave birth to many stories of
friendship with the sun
and delightful play with long, slow-melting days.
Autumn was woven out of multicolored visitors
who brought brilliant memories of lingering warmth,
turned cool in the waiting.
And Winter too was certainly marked with its own tales,
though admittedly they held much pain
for they flowed out of loneliness and were written in tears.

Once the snows of Winter had passed,
the people waited for the season of Spring,
for they knew the cycle had been set,
and only Spring could be the passage from Winter to Summer.
Thus they waited.
The sun returned; its warmth blossomed; flowers shone.
And still they waited.

In the boredom of waiting for Spring to journey through their land,
the people took to other interests.
They began to plant gardens,
thinking of the days to come
when they would gather to share the fruits of harvest.
They dreamed of seasons passed
and daydreamed new shapes for future days.
As they danced with the hills
and skipped over clouds
and played leapfrog with woodland waterfalls,

34

they delighted in the freedom that comes when one escapes Winter.
They fell in love and rejoiced.
It seemed as if a new life-giving fever
possessed those who waited for Summer.
It was during this time that a lone troubadour
minstrelled his way through their waiting.
He sang all of the songs sung by the troubadours of other seasons,
yet somehow he was new.
He was young, though he seemed to have the wisdom of age.
He belonged to the future, though he came from the past.
He was a stranger, though all seemed to have known him before.
They spoke often of this new troubadour,
but always they would shrug their shoulders,
curious about his purpose,
for he seemed to have come to do more than sing songs.

There were a chosen few, however,
who heard a song unheard by any of the others who waited.
It was only later that this came to be known, however, —
later when they would dare share their strange experiences.
Always the song would be heard
but the singer never seen,
though they would recognize the voice as that of the troubadour.
Always the song would come,
as they later came to realize,
when they were taken up in their activities of waiting,
when they were planting,
or dreaming,
or delighting in their freedom,
or lost in youthful love.
Always the song accompanied one of these moments:

   Of a people born to Summer
      is the song that I now sing,
   sharing peace and joy and laughter
      and the love that they all bring.

Those people made a journey
   through Autumn and her days,
and carried always with them
   colored memories filled with praise.

After Autumn, Winter followed,
   and the people cried in fear,
for they missed the joys of Summer,
   a friend who'd once been near.

This song which I now sing
   bears a gift to you today,
perhaps a blessing, or a curse;
   it is for you to say.
Though never heard a second time,
the ballad was never forgotten
for always the final verse would startle and confuse
and often even frighten
since no one understood the gift.
Each hoped it to be a blessing
and feared it to be a curse,
yet were distraught over not knowing how to choose.

The strange order of occurrences came to be discovered
when the wise one in the community came upon a child
quietly weeping in a hidden corner of clouded sunlight.
It was then that the child told the story
of the song
and the gift.
In the silence that waited,
one by one the others who had also heard the song came forth
to tell their own tales of the song
and how they too had come to be gifted —
though whether that gift was a blessing or a curse
none could say.

After all had told their story,
only the silence was left to speak.

In that silence one more story remained to be told.
There, seated on a branch of a tree high above them all,
sat the troubadour.
Softly he began his song for the people gathered below:

Of a people born to Summer
   is the song that I once sang,
sharing peace and joy and laughter
   and the love from which they sprang.

Then, as quickly as he had begun,
the troubadour grew silent.
The people strained to see the strange minstrel
who had brought such confusion and fear
while they waited for Spring to lead them into Summer.
It was the wise one who spoke first,
asking for the meaning of all that had taken place.
Then, once more, out of the gentle silence,
the minstrel again began to sing:
To those who heard the song I sang
   a gift you did receive;
whatever your care as you heard the tale
   then that you are able to achieve.

To those aworking in God's rich earth,
   'tis a blessing to have much to share,
but also a curse, if one should hoard
   and never take time to care.

If you were filled with new born dreams
   when I sang my ballad to you,
then you'll either have visions and be able to lead,
   or you'll die alone — adieu.

If when I sang you felt most free,
   then bring that gift to all in life,
for if you choose yourself instead,
   then you shall know much strife.

And finally love was also given,
    so others too might love,
but if it turns to lust and self —
    you've failed, by God above.

The people stood stunned now realizing
how the spirits of some had been touched by the troubadour
and how indeed a gift had been given.
And then they cried out to the troubadour above,
"Why did not all receive the gift,
for it does not seem fair that some should be gifted
and others remain barren?"

The troubadour then explained to the people gathered below him.
"You have spent much time waiting for Spring
and for the birth of new life;
and in your waiting your spirits turned to new fancies —
to the earth
and to dreaming,
to your freedom
and to new love.
But you should now know,
and thus I will tell you,
that I am the season of Spring for whom you have so long waited.
Know also that to each of you
I sang the ballad of the gift
with its blessing and its curse.
That is why each of you shares
in the fever and the excitement of Spring and my gifts."
"If that is true," the people asked,
"why did not all of us hear the tale you sang?"

"The reason you did not hear," replied the troubadour,
"is because, in your distractions and in your fantasies,
you did not also take time to listen to the world about you.
Thus it was that your new found delights
lured you from the wisdom which Springtime always offers.

Yet because you are new born,
I now promise that to each of you
the ballad shall be sung one more time,
once more in every lifetime.
It may come when you are young
or perhaps in the wisdom of your age,
perhaps when you are 7 or 17 or 70,
but it shall come;
and for you who hear its tale,
then you shall know your gift as well.
Yet if again you are deaf to all that life speaks
and you do not hear the tale,
it may be that unknowingly you will allow your gift to become a curse.
Listen closely, then, for such is my promise to you,
that before your final day
my melody shall be sung to each of you
and to those who will follow you as well —
once in every lifetime:

     To those who hear the song I sing
          a gift you will receive;
     whatever your care as you hear the tale,
          then that you'll be able to achieve."

The ballad ended, and the troubador disappeared
with as much mystery as when he first arrived.
Spring had come and had journeyed among the people
and now had left to make room for Summer's return.
Summer did come home,
and the friend to which they all had first been gifted embraced them
with sun and warmth and joy and laughter.

Thus the tale of the troubadour of Spring has come to an end,
but you who read this tale or hear it told must also know
that once in every lifetime
the tale is sung again.
In the Springtime of every year
listen, then, with care

lest you be deaf to the tune and never know your gift
of the fruit of the earth,
or the dreams of new days,
or the freedom of life,
or of a love that stays.

In the middle
when we begin again

The
Waiting
Season

Advent is the waiting season,
>   hoping to be rediscovered.
>   She is seasoned waiting,
>   wishing wisdom
>   and pregnant with promised life.
>   She is a season conceived each day,
>   yet so often dying
>   without ever having been born.
We wait
>   and Advent waits
>   but they are two different times
>   onesobusy
>   and
>   one
>   quite
>   still.

We wait
   for Christmas and her certificated gifts
      for cards, repeating year old wishes turned stale
            by necessity
      for parties and their cocktailed people
         for carols and their promises of recorded joy.
We wait
   and Advent dies
      for they are two different times
         onesobusy
           and
           one
          quite
          still.
Advent, the waiting season,
        dies, seasoned with waiting
           but never tasted.
She waits,
    hoping that we might walk into the Lord
        hand in hand.
She dies,
    waiting for us
       hoping that we might wait with her
       but we have not yet learned how to wait.
Advent waits
the Lord waits
    and they find each other,
for waiting can only be celebrated by waiting
and because we have not yet learned how to wait,
       Advent dies,
         seasoned with waiting
         yet never tasted.

The
Bag
Lady

Doorbells and presents are always filled with surprises, perhaps because they both come wrapped in the unexpected. And when the doorbell is the occasion for a gift, the delight in our spirits often multiplies to such intensity that once again we thrill at the child within. This is one such story. However, I caution you that though it is a story about children, it will ask you to transform your innocence into courage.

The doorbell rang and as I opened the door, I found standing there an older lady, looking very much like one of the bag-ladies of State Street in Milwaukee. They carry all that they own in shopping bags and, for the most part, support themselves by asking for quarters and nickels and dimes from passers-by. That person who came to my door was very

much like such a bag-lady. She said to me, "Could I please talk to you?" In the back of my mind I thought I knew what it was she wanted to talk about — a quarter or a dollar or what she then needed. Nevertheless, I said, "Sure!" and invited her in to be seated.

"I would like to give you something," she began. "In fact there are two things I would like to give you." I thought such a comment to be rather inside-out for usually the bag-ladies come asking, yet this one came offering. "I would like to give to you a story," she continued, "but it is a very different kind of story for it goes back a long way. It happened before you were born. It happened before I was born, before our mothers and fathers were born. It happened a long, long time ago — I don't even remember the years anymore.

"In a land far, far away, there was a tucked-away village. There in the center of that village was a small table, and on that table there was always a loaf of bread. Yet no one ever ate of the bread; no one ever took the bread. For, you see, there were all kinds of stories which roamed about the village — stories of people who had taken the bread and had become slaves. Thus no one took the bread for fear of becoming a slave. Other stories told of people who had taken the bread and had disappeared. Thus no one took the bread for fear of being seen no more. Still other stories were told of people who had taken the bread and had died. Thus no one ever took the bread for fear that they too would die. No one ever remembered who it was who had taken the bread and had become a slave or had disappeared or had died, but they did remember the stories, and that was all that mattered.

There was a ritual in this village that whenever a young boy or a young girl turned fourteen they would be brought to the table in the center of the village. There the elder of the village would stand opposite the youth with the table between them, and all of the other villagers would gather around. The elder would then ask the young boy or the young girl, 'Do you wish to take the bread?' Always out of fear of becoming a slave or of disappearing, or of dying, the young boy or the young girl would say, 'No.' Three times the elder would ask the young person, simply to make sure the question was clearly understood. Always the young person would answer three times, 'No'."

As the bag-lady went on, I thought to myself of how strange this story

46

was. Yet a long time ago I discovered that when stories come from places you do not expect, they often bear truth within them.

The bag-lady went on. "One day a young boy turned fourteen and was brought forth to the table in the center of the village. As prescribed by the ritual the elder stood opposite the young boy, and all of the people of the village gathered around. The elder looked at the young boy and asked, 'Do you wish to take the bread?' This time the young boy said, 'Yes'. In surprise the people all gasped for no one had ever said yes. Then the elder inquired once more, 'Do you wish to take the bread?' Again the boy replied, 'Yes.' One more time, having explained all of the different stories about slavery and disappearance and death, the elder asked, 'Do you wish to take the bread?' For the third time the boy said, 'Yes'. Then everyone in the village stepped back. The boy walked forward, and he took the bread in his hands.

"What happened in the days that followed," said the bag-lady, "is that the boy didn't become a slave. What did happen is that he began to go about doing all kinds of good for people, good that no one else would ever do for anyone. You might say that he became more of a servant, for anything that anyone would ask he would do. And he did disappear for a while. Not forever, but it seems that as the stories came back to the village, he was among the people telling them about a God who loved them so deeply that no matter what they would do, he would still love them. Then one day he did return. And you ask, 'Did he die?' Well, because the boy would do anything for anyone, and because he went about telling them about a God who loved them, and because it disturbed the people so much that they could not be what he invited them to be, one day they did kill him. Yet the word soon spread among the people that he still lived among them."

Then, suddenly, the bag-lady got up from her chair and walked out the door. I began to follow her, but she left quickly. As I came back inside bewildered, I noticed, then, that she had left her bag. Carrying the sack, I ran out the door and to the street, but there was no one out there. I looked up and down the street, unable to understand how someone could disappear so quickly. Then, holding her bag, I walked back inside thinking about her story and about the boy who once took the bread. Not knowing what was in her bag and without even looking, I reached in to see what it was she had left. Suddenly I was frightened, for I found bread in the bag and realized then that I too had now taken the bread. I began to wonder if I would become a slave, if I would disappear to be seen no more, or if I too would soon die. In the end it crossed my mind that perhaps this was the bag-lady's second gift. I could not help but wonder if perhaps she and that young boy of fourteen were the same person.

One day soon, before a week of days has passed, someone will come to you and offer you bread. Then you too will have to decide whether or not you will take the bread. In that moment remember the story of the bag-lady and remember, too, how we are asked to die each day for one another. Above all else, however, when someone comes and offers you bread, consider for a moment what life would be if no one ever took the bread. Then, having considered such a possibility — decide and choose.

The Elf
the Leprechaun
and
the Bargain

It happened on a night when an elf journeyed from the North and a leprechaun journeyed from the South and both happened to meet at the point where the East touches the West. There, at the center of life, on a night robbed of its stars and left to be guarded by the dimly watchful moon, the course of love was changed; and ever since that night we live with the consequences of that chance meeting.

Though unknown to one another, both the elf and the leprechaun were traveling to the land of the other with the hope of striking a bargain — "all of our wealth for all of your love". Yet at the moment of their meeting a most unusual occurrence took place. There at the center of life, where North and South and East and West are one, at that point all is transparent. What one dreams cannot be obscured. What one strives for

51

cannot be concealed. Thus both the elf and the leprechaun each came clothed in the same designs, unaware that their garb revealed rather than concealed. Immediately they both perceived the stalemate. The wealth with which they were prepared to barter no longer held any power, and the love which they sought became locked in their own selfish passion.

Aware of their impasse, they called to the moon, hoping for a solution from the one responsible for the course of the night. The moon only waned and slipped with a nod into the wind who carried them both — the elf and the leprechaun — to the God who had shaped the hearts of all creation.

Once before the giver of life, they described their planned deception and the revelation which had taken place at the center of life where North meets with South and East with West and each with the other. Since God had been at that center, their explanation would not have been necessary; but because he is not visible to those who journey blindly, he listened with patience to their quest for all love in exchange for all wealth. It was a most unusual desire, thought God, and certainly a step forward, for most often it is wealth that is sought in exchange for real love. Yet God could not help but perceive that their desire for all love was prompted by a wish to love all creation and thereby to control as well as to serve and to own as well as to be owned.

With gentleness and with wisdom God then promised to the elf and to the leprechaun both, and to those from whom they had journeyed and to their descendants all, that from that day hence they would always be filled with all the love they could bear.

The elf and the leprechaun both rejoiced in their gift and in the fact as well that their offer of all wealth had not been demanded in payment. Each traveled home, one to the North and one to the South, to announce the good news that all love was now theirs. Joyful celebration followed in song and in dance among all the elves and all the leprechauns. Yet there was also the unspoken awareness that what was offered as a gift also bore a strange anxiety and fear.

In times to come new suns burned, and new moons guarded the night, and seasons became unraveled and rewoven. Now people live in the hollows and hills where once only elves and leprechauns grew old and sometimes wise, and we who have followed them share both their gift and their fear.

Indeed, love is a gift freely given. In truth, it is a blessing from God, for if he had accepted from the elf and the leprechaun their payment of all wealth, we would always live with the suspicion that given enough wealth we could buy love, simply because God had once entered into such a bargain with his people. Instead God did gift us with his love, and he gave it to us freely.

However, love also comes colored with fear, for while we are all called to the gift, each of us must travel first through the center of life where all that we are is transparent and clearly known. Though fearful, it is only in that center that we can know the joys of love, for only in that center does fear lose all meaning. To that place each of us travels, called to the center of life where once an elf and a leprechaun met with a bargain.

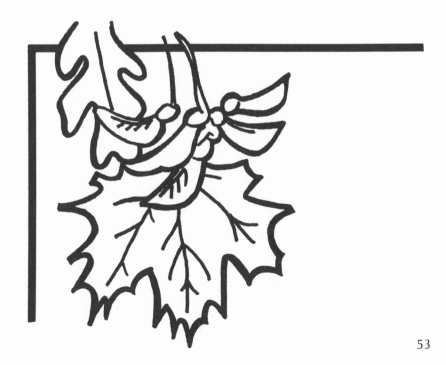

Michael

In the middle of our city, almost as if it had been lost there, having fallen from someone's pocket of wishes, there is a green, wooded daydream by the name of Hawthorne Glen. I go there on occasion to be alone, to pray, to smile at God's playtime. What I am about to tell you, you may or may not believe. Yet all I can say is that with all my heart I know it to be true and, therefore, must conclude that it really happened.

It took place in the days immediately before Easter, and I had come to Hawthorne Glen to find an Easter message to share with the people who believe. Having pathed the glen emptyhearted and messageless, I sat down on an old stump, long tinted with moss. Like a chameleon, the daytime was about to turn color and become evening when I heard a voice call out, "Hello!" I turned and there, right by my side, was a small,

54

short man. He was very short — about ten inches tall, twelve at the most. Without asking, he hopped up onto my knee, looked up into my eyes and said with all the assurance of someone who knew, 'I'll give you a message."

"How do you know I'm looking for a message?" I wondered out loud. "And who are you? What's your name?"

"My name is Michael," he said, answering my last question first. "And the reason I know what you're looking for is because I'm an angel."

"Oh, you're an angel........," I mumbled — not agreeing and not really asking, but filling up space with wondering-time.

He caught the searching in my eyes quickly and said, "You don't believe me, do you?"

"Well........," I wasn't sure and, to be honest, I was a little afraid. "........you don't look like an angel. Angels are supposed to be dressed in white, and you're not dressed in white."

"Who told you angels are dressed in white?" he shouted back, and then sent silence to wait for an answer.

"Well, you don't have any wings, either," said I — having known for a long time that all angels have wings.

"Who told you angels have wings?" he shouted back once more, and then sent more silence.

"Well angels are tall and young, and you're so short and...."

"Who told you angels are tall and young?" he shouted, almost falling off of my knee. I suddenly realized, then, the mistake of what I'd said. "Do you want to know the secret, or don't you?" he insisted, quieting down and trying to appear dignified.

"Oh, I do," I said, suddenly realizing that the Easter message was going to be a secret. "Oh, but I'm not very good at keeping secrets," I confessed.

"That's OK," said Michael — to my surprise. "This is a different kind of secret. I can only tell you if you promise to tell someone else and make

56

them promise to do the same when they tell the secret to someone they know. Is it a deal?" He was getting excited now. "Do you promise? Huh? Do you want to know the secret?"

"Oh, I do," I said. "And I promise. I promise I'll tell someone else."

It was then that Michael whispered his secret to me — and a grand secret it was too, well worth the price of agreeing to pass it on to another. He whispered it so quietly that I had to turn my head so that my ear could get close enough to hear. And by the time I turned back to smile my Thank You, Michael had disappeared. He simply wasn't there — gone as quickly and as mysteriously as he had arrived. I sat there, all alone, holding a new secret in my heart, excited and thrilled with the privilege. And so it is that I tell you this Easter story — to keep my promise to Michael and share the secret of Easter which he gave.

There is only one condition, however, (as you perhaps well know by now) if you wish to know the secret, and that is that you must agree to pass on the secret to another so that the message of Easter does not die. If, then, you wish to know the secret, and if you agree to tell another, then finish this story and read to the end. If, however, you question its truth or hesitate to say "yes", then for you the story of Michael and his Easter secret must end here. Choose now — this ending or the secret which follows.

*   *   *   *

I am delighted that you chose to know the secret, for it is indeed a most marvelous secret that tells why Easter is, why God did send His Son, and why we sing Alleluia all day long. This, then, is the secret of Michael, the secret of Easter — God Loves You. Because you too now know the secret, it is for you to spread the word as you promised so that all the world will know the Good News of Easter Day.

> This story can easily be told with the children gathered around sitting on the sanctuary floor and steps. When it comes to telling them the secret (and they will always agree to the conditions) whisper the secret to them and send them out into the congregation to tell all the grown-up children in the pews the secret just received. What follows, then, is what Easter is all about — the Good News of the Gospel carried to all the corners of the earth, to all the peoples of God's creation.

Traces
Of
Stars

Every people, every culture has ghost stories. They are not always called such, but they are stories of spirits and strange happenings and fright-filled events of wonder. The Hebrew people, too, had their own such tales (call them ghost stories if you wish), and for the most part they can be found in the Books of Daniel and Revelation and parts of the Gospels. What follows is a story about Hebrew spirits.

It was quite a while ago that I told you a story about an angel by the name of Michael whom I had met. No more than twelve inches tall — to be sure, I met him then in a green, wooded, daydream land named Hawthorne Glen. When I first met him the snow had just begun to weep with old age, and soon thereafter the snow did die for one more year.

It was a warm summer night months later when I returned to Hawthorne Glen, hoping that I once again might meet the Michael who called himself an angel. On that night the stars seemed to beacon their light through the darkness, and the unrolled sky warmed the earth with its beauty. It was a grand night. I lay on my back in the middle of a huge field, taking in the sky and wondering how all of those stars found their way up into the sky's blanket.

With the suddeness of a moment I heard a voice say, "I can tell you." "Who said that?" I blurted out. "I did," came back the answer. "Who's you?" I wanted to know. "It's me, Michael. Don't you remember me? I'm the angel. Remember?"

"Oh! Sure, I remember," now relieved of my fright and even delighted that my wish to see Michael again had come true. "I can tell you," said Michael again. "You can tell me what?" I wanted to know. "I can tell you how all those stars got up into the sky."

I was startled. "How did you know I was wondering that?" "Because I am an angel, and angels know what people wonder, that's how," was Michael's reply. "OK," I said, satisfied that he had the answer. "Tell me how all those stars got up there."

"A long, long time ago when all of creation had just been born, and God was busy shaping and reshaping, he formed a huge sun out of his fiery love and tossed it high up into the sky. Then, shortly after, he formed the moon and placed it in the sky as well. Yet because it took a while for the moon to begin glowing brightly and because God had not yet decided upon stars, the nighttime sky was black and dark.

"During this time all of the people were good. They were always gentle with one another, and they always forgave. They would always take time to show each other they cared, and they would always rejoice in the gifts they had been given. But that is when the ghosts began to wander through the land. Once in a while a ghost would come pounding on someone's door — bam, bam, bam. The people who lived there would hurry to look out, and always no one would be there. The people on whose door the ghost had pounded were sure it was their neighbor playing tricks, so they stopped being gentle because they were not going to allow anyone to frighten them. Other ghosts would come and start people's homes on fire. Always, after the people put out the fires, they blamed their neighbors for lighting the fires and would refuse to forgive them.

Other ghosts would fly over gardens and scatter weed seeds among the flowers and vegetables. The people, then, became so busy pulling the weeds out of their gardens that no one had time to care for anyone else. Then too some ghosts would whisper all sorts of things in people's ears — ideas about how so-and-so owned this, and so-and-so had just gotten a new that. Soon people began to grow greedy, and no one was happy with the gifts that they had been given.

"Well," said Michael, "I became so worried and anxious about all of those people who were losing their goodness because of the spooks and ghosts, that I decided I somehow had to save them." "What did you do?" I asked. "That part of the story is in this book of stories," said Michael. "If you open it you can read all about it." I did open the book and this is what I found.

> At that time there shall arise
> 　Michael, the great prince,
> 　guardian of your people;
> It shall be a time unsurpassed in distress
> 　since nations began until that time.
> At that time your people shall escape,
> 　everyone who is found written in the book.
> Many of those who sleep
> 　in the dust of the earth shall awake;
> Some shall live forever,
> 　others shall be an everlasting horror and disgrace.
> But the wise shall shine brightly
> 　like the splendor of the firmament,
> And those who lead the many to justice
> 　shall be like the stars forever.
>
> Dan 12:1-3

I sat there amazed and filled with wonder, thinking, "That's fantastic, Michael; you gathered together all of the good people and carried them up into the heavens. And all of the good people became stars in the heavens and their goodness keeps on shining. That's really great, Michael." When I turned to tell Michael of my wonder, he was gone. I looked up into the sky hoping to see him, but instead I saw a star falling to earth. I wondered, then, what good person fell to earth and why. Then I saw another falling star.....and another. I thought perhaps Michael would tell me, but he was not around to explain. Often during that summer I saw other stars fall, and each time I had wished Michael were nearby.

Before long, summer breathed her last warmth, and soon November followed. November, as you know, comes gloomy and cloudy, as if someone had darkened the sun, as if the moon had lost her light. In November there are not any stars in the sky — only darkness. Thus I journeyed back to Hawthorne Glen and I laid on my back again — in the middle of the same open field. Suddenly I heard, "Swishhh, swishhh, swishhh." "Who's there?" I shouted out. "It's us," came the hushed answer. "Who's us?" I wanted to know. "It's us — the four angels." "You are? Where'd you come from?" I insisted.

"My name is Frigor, and I'm the angel of the North," answered the first. Then another spoke up, "My name is Aurora, and I'm the angel of the South." "And me, I'm Timor, and I'm the angel of the West." "And I'm Solar, and I'm from the East. We're the four angels of the four corners of the earth." Then to my surprise he said, "We can tell you why there are falling stars and where they go." I was amazed. "How did you know I was wondering that?" "Because we're angels, silly; don't you know? Angels can tell what you're wondering." "Oh," I mumbled, suddenly recalling how Michael had once said the same. "Well tell me," I asked, "why does the sun get darkened, and why does the moon lose her light, and why do the stars fall from the sky? If you know, tell me."

"It's easy," said the four angels. "You see, after God's creation began running smoothly, God put us in charge of the four corners to make sure all of the people were doing good things. Well, we would send out our winds to check up on people to see how they were doing, except that we had to send a lot of clouds to cover the sun and the moon, or else people would see our winds doing their checking. So that's why the sun gets darkened and why the moon loses her light. Whenever any of the winds find people needing some goodness, they come and tell us. Then each of us gets at one corner of the heavens, and all together we start shaking the sky like a big blanket. As we shake it, some of the stars bounce out and fall to the ground. Those falling stars are the goodness that the people need, stars of gentleness and forgiveness and joy and caring."

It sounded so funny that I started laughing then and said, "That's not true." "Yes it is," they all insisted. "No, that's too silly," and I simply laughed some more. It was then that they began to leave, with the sound of their voices trailing in the night as they shouted, "Look in the book.........look in the book....."

I went back to the book, the book of stories that Michael had given me, and this is what I found:

Jesus said to his disciples: "During that period
after trials of every sort the sun will be darkened,
the moon will not shed its light, stars will fall out
of the skies, and the heavenly hosts will be shaken.
Then men will see the Son of Man coming in the clouds
with great power and glory. He will dispatch his
messengers and assemble his chosen from the four winds,
from the farthest bounds of the earth and sky."

Mk 13:24-27

When I finished, I turned from the book and all that I saw was a sack. I opened the sack and in it there was a star, and another star, and more and more stars — all kinds of fallen stars, stars of gentleness and forgiveness, stars of caring and stars of joy — a sack of goodness to share with everyone.

*   *   *   *

You see, every star is part of the goodness that Michael had collected and placed in the sky. They are all part of God's kingdom that is among us, because God's kingdom is not only something that is going to happen when we die. God's kingdom is already happening. So when you are gentle, God's kingdom is happening. And when you forgive, God's kingdom is happening. And when you take time to care, God's kingdom is happening. And when you are happy with the gifts you already have,

God's kingdom is happening. You see, Jesus began God's kingdom, and we are his kingdom. It has already begun.

After all of that, I went back to the book of stories Michael had given me and read from it one last time.

"Learn a lesson from the fig tree. Once the sap of its branches runs high and it begins to sprout leaves, you know that summer is near. In the same way, when you see these things happening, you will know that he is near, even at the door. I assure you, this generation will not pass away until all these things take place. The heavens and the earth will pass away, but my words will not.

"As to the exact day or hour, no one knows it, neither the angels in heaven nor even the Son, but only the Father."

Mk 13:28-32

This is the gospel of the Lord

This story is based upon and built
around the scripture readings for the
thirty-third Sunday of the Year, cycle B.
It originally served in its entirety
as the Liturgy of the Word for a children's
celebration on that Sunday

At the point in the story marked by
* * * *, a sack was opened containing
multi-colored stars bearing the
messages "be gentle" or "forgive" or
"take time to care" or "rejoice in
your gifts". The children who were gathered
about were asked to pass the stars out
to everyone present. That having taken place
the story then continued to its conclusion.

Castles
On
Marco Polo

Marco Polo was not always as it is now. There was a time when she was yet what she had always been — a relatively unmarred remnant of the Creator's love — allowed to drift lazily along the Gulf Coast of America's mainland. Hawks and owls sewed the sky to the earth by day and by night, with salt water marshes providing an ever stocked pantry easily unlocked by the swiftness of the scavengers. Hammocks of lush sub-tropical vegetation had not yet been relegated to supposedly generous reservations. Mango forests were yet to be reduced to tourista woods, and manatees swam the salt water inlets unthreatened by the butchering blades of motorboat propellers. The bleached, rough-hewn beaches gently carved by razor sharp waves and strewn with shavings of seashelled life ribboned the island as a gift for those who dwelt there. Marco Polo Island was once an island for dreamers.

It was perhaps tragically inevitable that she should be discovered by those whose dreams came true with the accumulation of wealth rather than with sharing beauty. But such it was. In order to build con-dominiumed sanctuaries for the northern snowbirds who could afford them, salt water marshes were drained by concrete channels, scars of the developer's surgical knife. High rises competed with royal palms to dominate the sky line — and in time conquered those majestic natives. And while the beaches still glittered, it was no longer because they were strewn with shells of the sea but rather with the flip-top shells of artificial refreshment. Yet what was most tragic was the effect upon the people who lived on Marco Polo Island — the simple island dwellers who had once been taught to believe in the wealth of beauty rather than the beauty of wealth. This is their story — yet it is a story that belongs to each of us.

As I have said, the island dwellers of Marco Polo were dreamers. There were those who dreamt with the pen as well as those with the brush. There were lovers of the sea and lovers of life, and of course those who were simply lovers. All dreamers of one sort or another, they were believers in peace and in justice and in goodness. They believed in the human person.

Yet when those seeking to make a profit from that island innocence began to market their dream, the islanders paid the purchase price. They forfeited one dream in order to acquire another. Thus commercialism, which was once a foreigner, became a naturalized citizen, and Marco Polo Island surrendered her innocence.

On a misty morning, shortly after the first high rise had been completed and the canals carved, one of the island dwellers discovered a portion of the island beach magically dotted with sand castles — square ones and round ones, high castles and low castles, some turreted and some with moats. There were dozens, even hundreds, perhaps a thousand castles in the sand, all different, all exquisite, all perfect. The islander ran back to the village to announce his discovery. He rang the steeple bell and shouted to the people leaning from their windows. He interrupted the dreamers and woke the lovers and excited the village. They all ran to the beaches, but in the time that had passed, the tide had come in and claimed the works of the unknown medieval architect.

68

Some thought it a hoax, and others simply laughed at the islander who had made the castled discovery. "Just a dreamer from days passed," they said and returned home to their new found dreams. A few, however, believed in the islander, and so together they rose early the next morning to search the beaches. And they were not unrewarded, for they found the beach just as it had been described the morning before — a fairyland of turreted castles built from sand. They roamed that enchanted land, mesmerized by its beauty and detail. Then, as the tide again rose, they were forced to retreat and watch the sea slowly but deliberately conquer the sandy defenses.

That day the islanders told the others of what they had seen, and in the day that followed all of the villagers made their trek into that new unknown country visited upon their shores. They delighted in their gift but wondered who the giver might be. They drew lots to stand watch at night and discover who the builder of the castles could be. But always the sun rose to announce their failure. Either the castled village would appear on some other portion of the island beach, or it would be built while night clouds slipped past the moon and blinded their vision with darkness. No one seemed to know who it was that built the castles in the sand.

Weeks passed and were woven into months, and still the castles continued to be built in the sand. Yet they had become so commonplace that the islanders no longer got up early to go to the beach, nor did they continue to try to discover who was responsible for them. Occasionally, one or two would survive the high tide, only to be destroyed by those who walked the beaches. "There will always be more," they would say. In the end, it seemed the castles had failed for, whatever their purpose, they were ignored.

The days turned Autumn and began to slip into darkness earlier and earlier, and the southern sun grew lazy in her daily climb. Fewer people now came to the sea. Yet on one of those days, a young child by the name of Jenny built her own castle on a portion of the sandy shore stolen from the waves. So taken up in her defense of the castle from the waves, she never noticed the stranger marching toward her fortress. A gentle lover of the sea, he had grown old and wise, and now sought someone with whom to share the gift of his years. He stopped and stood at the moat Jenny had built to calm the threatening sea. "Would you like some help?" he asked with his smile. "If you want to," she smiled back. And thus it was that Jenny began to learn the skills of castle building from the gentle island stranger.

"Mister," she asked, "how come you can do this so good?" "Oh, that's not so important," was the old islander's reply. "All that matters is that you too learn how, for everyone else has forgotten, and the island needs a castle builder." But Jenny didn't understand; the old islander could see the questions in her eyes. He knew, too, that she wondered if he was the castle builder no one had ever met. And so it was that he began to share with her the secret and the reason for his nightly visits to the island shore.

"You see, Jenny, I've lived on this island for a long time. I love her and her gift, but most of all I love her people. For as long as I have lived, the people of Marco Polo have been dreamers. Day after day, Jenny, they lived their dreams — dreams of love for their families and kindness for their neighbors. While others dreamed of conquering by war, the islanders here dreamed of peace. They dreamed of people never being hungry, even though they knew others dreamed of growing rich and gathering wealth. They dreamed of life for all — never of death; and they always forgave. The islanders, Jenny, have always been a good people.

"Then one day some strangers came to the island and brought with them strange dreams — dreams of wealth and comfort and success and power. And the islanders began to change their dreams, and with that the island changed as well. The marshes dried up and the birds no longer came to sing. The island began to die because the dreams had died. It was then that I thought, 'Perhaps if I built castles shaped like those dreams, perhaps the islanders will not forget. Perhaps some day they will return to their old dreams — the dreams that brought life to them and to the island.

"It was then that I began building castles in the sand, and I built them in the image of their dreams. I built them out of sand so that they would not be too rigid because dreams need to be reshaped as people's lives are reshaped. And I built them close to the sea, knowing that the sea would have her way and level them each morning. That way, Jenny, they would have to be rebuilt each day — like dreams — or else they begin to crum-

70

ble from lack of attention. I didn't build any big castles, either, because big castles look cold and frighten people away — just like oversized dreams. And each castle I shaped in the image of its own dream — castles with lots of windows and doors to make everyone feel welcome, and other castles with big courtyards for fun and good times, and then some with big fireplaces where people could sit and visit and just be friends. Then one day I decided to build them a bit further from the shore, hoping more people might see the castles and remember their old dreams. But they were just stepped on and knocked down. I guess it's difficult to face dreams of what we know we could be but don't want to try to be. So, Jenny, that's the story of the castles on Marco Polo Island. Now you know who it is who built them and the reason they were built."

"But why do you want me to build castles, mister? You know how to do them so much better than I can."

"Because, Jenny, I'm old, and I won't be here to build castles and dreams for many more days. And it's important that somebody still build them, at least every once in a while — just so that no one forgets the dreams. If the dreams die, nothing else matters Jenny. If you're willing to build castles, perhaps someone will remember the dreams."

"I can do it; I can build the castles, because you told me the story of the island, and Marco Polo is my island, too, just like it's yours."

*   *   *   *

The castles in the sand continued till the days turned Winter, and then they stopped. No one really noticed that they had ended until weeks later — no one except for Jenny. And when the islanders did finally realize the castles were no more, they simply shrugged their shoulders and thought it strange. Occasionally someone would find themselves on the island beach early in the morning and come across one or two castles, but never the hundreds that once were built there. Yet the one or two they did see were built in the image of a thousand dreams by a child who had made a promise because she loved an island and her people.

When next, then, you come upon a castle in the sand, step cautiously and miss not the dream it holds.

Love
Jonah

The sea can be a library of contradictions,
enticing with shelled shallows,
easy treasures of deceptively rapid wealth,
as well as magnificent with caverns of depth
known at the price of risk and fear.
She can be tranquil and insistent with the rhythm of the sun
as well as ravaging with unsatiated hunger and power.
Yet it was only with a vision reflected in time
that the man now grown old had come to understand her.
Thus, he had to confess, that his love for her
began with passion
and had resolved itself in his being tamed.

72

For three side-by-side days
he had gone to the sandy no-man's land,
the long established peacemaker between water and earth.
For three days he had watched a young boy
of no more than eight
weave a relationship with the sea
as he wandered in and out of her waves.
As he looked back, the boy and the sea had fallen in love,
neither the boy wishing to deny the sea of her wealth,
nor she attempting to assert her power over his youth.
By week's end
the two strange lovers shared a common dream.

It was on the fourth day of the week
that the boy took note
of the man's regular presence at the sea
and asked why it was that he always came to the sea.

In search of a sun tan
seemed a sufficient reply for an eight year-old,
though in truth there were other reasons
secreted in his daydreams.
The boy smiled then,
in a way that said he knew the old man's dreams,
and the old man wondered
if that were possible for one so young.

The boy lingered a while longer
as he shared skills for building castles out of sand,
while the old man's spirit transformed those castles into dreams.
Each sensed, however, that for both
their tasks of building castles and dreams
were quite identical.

On the following day they met again.
For a while the old man watched the boy
wandering over the shore and playing with the sea.
It seemed strange that the boy who came

only to be with the sea
found more shelled treasures
than those who came raking her rim with their eyes
searching for shelled jewels.
Always the boy would offer his find to one of the hoarders;
always he bore more gifts than they;
always they slipped the gift into their plastic-bagged vaults
and lusted for more.

Later that day, after he had hugged the sea good-by,
the boy paused to visit where the old man sat
and asked why they were so taken up with the shallows,
why they all spent so much time bent over,
gazing at their feet
and hoping that their eyes might stumble
upon more of what they already possessed.
The old man was not sure how to answer and hesitated.
In that moment the boy went on to explain
that the depths held so much more beauty
and goodness
and life,
if only they could see past the shallows.

Strange wisdom for a young boy, thought the old man,
and then asked how he had come upon such knowledge.

It was the sea who had taught him, explained the boy;
with him she shared her stories.
Then he hung his head;
a bit saddened by the hoarding he could not understand,
and wandered on home.

The following day they all gathered once more —
the boy,
the old man,
the shell gatherers,
and of course the sea.
The matinee drama of the day before was repeated,

though it was only the shell seekers, suspected the old man,
who were unaware of the plot and the major role
they collectively played.
This day the boy came by a bit sooner
and wondered again why it was that the old man came.

The wisdom he had shared demanded greater honesty,
and thus the old man felt comfortable
explaining his need to be stilled
by the harmony of the sun and sea
and how together they renewed him and his dreams.

The boy understood;
and that wisdom was reflected in his eyes.
The boy wondered, though,
trusting the old man now with a bit more of his wisdom,
why the old man could only find peace in the tranquil blend
of sun and sea.
It seemed to him
that there was also great beauty as well as love in the sea
when she was dark
and gray
and bold
in her flamboyant gestures.

The boy was right,
mused the old man,
one could be loved in strength
as well as in gentleness,
in honesty
as well as in kind acceptance.
It was another of the sea's contradictions
but also her wisdom.
Strange, he thought,
as well as a bit angered,
that such lessons should be known by an eight year old boy.
This day
as he left

76

LOVE,
JONAH

it was the old man who hung his head,
embarassed by his anger.

Two days remained and,
as it came to be,
two lessons as well,
On that day
born to be the second youngest of the week,
the Joseph of their days at the sea,
the boy
and the old man
as well as the others
all came again to court the sea —
some for her treasures,
some for her wisdom,
one simply for her loving presence.

Again the boy came by
and again he asked the old man why he had come.
So strange, it seemed,
to begin each day with the same question.
Yet always the old man's answer was different —
more honest,
more in need of wisdom.

Sometimes I come because I need to be cared for.
I come, if I am honest, in search of being loved.
I come flirting with humanity.
Having said that,
he wondered if he had said too much
or if one so young would understand.

If you come to find love, the young boy wondered,
why is it that you always come alone?
One only loves those one knows.
He went on to explain how he and the sea had become friends
and how they shared with one another their secrets.
But that was only because they had spent much time together,

78

because they were honest with one another.
He came to build her castles of jeweled sand,
content that she would gather them to herself,
never embarrassed by his generosity.
She offered to him life,
carried in the rhythm of the waves,
stealing the castles and offering him love.
But it was important that they be together.
People who come looking for shells, explained the boy,
do not come because they need to be loved,
or perhaps they come
hoping to be distracted in their need to be loved,
hoping to forget their loneliness.
The sea does teach both —
remembering
and
forgetting,
and in her gentleness
she lets the visitor decide.

How strange, this youth,
again he forced the old man's honesty
and again he colored it with truth.
Was it wisdom he held
or simply a reflection of the old man's heart?
Was it the boy
or the sea?
And why such contradictions?

The sun unfolded the final day
and with it the warmth that brought them altogether.
In the end the sea would continue to remain faithfully present;
the gatherers of shells would continue as well,
though always reinforced by an endless flow of new-comers;
only the man and the boy would depart at the end of the day,
each in search of paths homeward.

As the sky tired

and began to lose its grip on the sun,
the boy again stopped by.
This time it was the old man who asked the question.
Why had the boy come to the sea?

To say good-bye, answered the young boy,
to tell the sea he would not forget her,
that what they together had grown to become
would remain even in absence.
His spirit now had become one with hers.

As the boy built one final castle in the sand,
the old man daydreamed
of how the spirit of the sea
was much like God's spirit —
a horizon against which he came to know
life
and values
and indeed himself as well,
a horizon that breathed with the waves
the heartbeat of life,
perhaps even the heartbeat of God.
It was strange,
he thought to himself,
how he had come a week earlier as a shellseeker
and now left having discovered the beauty of life
contained in a willingness to journey deep.
He had come to be calmed
and would return less fearful of life's powerful tides.
He arrived alone
seeking to be loved
and soon would enter back into the only lives
where it could be found.
He had come fleeing God's spirit
and had been drawn into his spirit —
the rhythmic heartbeat of sea and waves.
They seemed all contradictions,
learned from a boy and the sea he had come to love.

80

The old man looked back
to give thanks to his young master,
but the young boy had left
while the old man had journeyed deep
into the storm of his own loneliness.
Where the boy had sat,
only a castle remained,
and in the sand he had written

                    Love, Jonah

Carved Out Of
Love
And Shaped Into
Seasons

Carved Out of Love and Shaped into Seasons

As summer grows heavy with life and warm afternoons begin to smell of autumn, children grow bored as they splash in shallow puddles of stagnant time. So it was with Greta and Andy as they slipped off in search of the wise Master of the Seasons. In their hearts they hoped to discover the secret of how to turn summer into autumn. They had been told that the Master lived in a cave wedged high on a mountain top near their home, and so the two began their climb.

Though their mountain was no more than a very high hill, it was heavily wooded and draped in strings of beaded boulders and jagged rocks. For eight year-old Greta as well as for Andy, two years her junior, the hill was indeed a mountain. If they followed the path, they had been told, and remained true all of the way to the top and then began their descent

down the dark side of the mountain until they came to the trunk of a large oak shaped in the form of a standing bear, if they would then leave the path in the direction of the wind for twenty blinks and then spin for as long as it takes to make a wish, they would stand facing the cave of the Master of the Seasons. They had memorized the route and had indeed been faithful to the instructions. Now, to their surprise, they stood before a cave which they believed belonged to the Master of the Seasons.

Just as they had been told, it was not dark and gloomy like other caves, but instead a warm, friendly light shown from inside. No sooner had they stepped inside, than they heard a voice so loud that Greta and Andy were not sure there was room in the cave for both them and the voice. "You've come for the secret, haven't you?" questioned the voice. They still had not seen who it was who spoke; but suddenly they grew embarrassed, wondering if their reason for coming was not proper.

More out of fear than out of courage, Andy spoke up. "Yes, it's true, whoever you are. We've come to pull the lever that turns summer into autumn. Will you show us how?"

The voice answered with a smile, and Greta and Andy were no longer afraid, even though they still had not discovered who it was who owned the voice. Then, with a whisper of light, they were twirled about, and there they stood in front of the Master of the Seasons. A most gentle Master he was indeed for the summer sun shown bright when he smiled, and spring played peek-a-boo in his eyes. He stood tall, crowned with sparkles of winter and robed in a cape of autumn rainbows carved from gold and orange and red — a most friendly Master. "There is no lever to turn summer into autumn." "Then perhaps a knob we could pull?" persisted Andy. "No such knob either," replied the Master, "only a secret."

"A secret," bubbled Greta. "Would you tell us? Please? Please tell us. We won't tell anyone. We promise." By now Andy was so excited that he simply overflowed with "Me too! Me too!"

"Very well," agreed the Master, as he invited Greta and Andy to sit down with him in the center of the light that filled his cave. All having been filled with light, the Master began. "Summer turns to winter as it journeys through autumn....." "No, No," interrupted Andy. "Summer turns into autumn, not into winter."

"Not so," replied the Master of the Seasons. "Not so! Though such is what many think. During the days of summer the lives of everyone are filled with fun and excitement, and all of God's people are free to make dreams come true. Yet there comes a time when people must return home to where their spirits first found life, when new dreams must be born and old dreams reconsidered. There must be a time to become one with another once again. There must be a time of winter, or we would remain summer-free all our lives.

"If you wish to journey into winter," continued the Master of the Seasons, "three conditions you must fulfill. There is no other way."

"We will; we will!" both Greta and Andy excitedly agreed. "Very well, then," explained the Master, "these are the three. First, you must agree to follow the wind wherever it leads you — however high among cloud-filled dreams, however low among once-upon-a-could've's. If you follow the wind, then you will live with my spirit. Second, you must live not only in the light but also walk without fear into darkness for the days will grow heavy. The third condition is this — you must be willing to let go of the warmth and live within the cold. Touched by the cold, you will find others who also seek warmth, and together then you will begin to be one people with one dream and one story to tell again and again. If you do these three, then you will find winter. Do you promise?"

When the Master finished explaining Greta and Andy stood silent, now a bit frightened and not so sure they wanted the secret of turning summer into winter. They would have rather chosen autumn as the successor to summer and not known the secret. Yet they had asked to know the secret and had promised as well not to tell anyone else. Unsure and quiet, they both agreed.

As Greta and Andy stepped out of the cave and back into the seasons, the wind turned summersaults in Andy's hair, and Greta buttoned her sweater against the cold, pulling it close around her neck. They hurried home down the mountainside, for already the day was almost asleep as the shadows began to pull the nighttime over their village — indeed much sooner than they had expected. The master had been right; the secret was coming true.

Each week that followed was painted with less and less summer and more and more winter. All but Greta and Andy kept speaking of autumn; only they knew the secret; only they understood the meaning of those days as summer journeyed through autumn into winter.

Finally winter did arrive. The winds first nudged and then pushed people indoors. Darkness slipped into every corner, and the cold drove everyone to gather with family and friends about their fires. Marvelous happenings soon began to take place. Family bonds of love were renewed. Dreams that had been misplaced or forgotten were rediscovered. People sang with the wind. Loneliness was overcome and the darkness lost its power. Laughter and happiness danced with the home fires and the cold could not break through. Indeed winter had once more brought everyone home and dressed them in love.

As winter took root, so did winter's people. In time Greta and Andy grew restless and once more journeyed up their mountain, traveling the same route as the time before. Down the dark side of the mountain they came, to the trunk of the oak shaped like a bear, following the wind for twenty blinks, and spinning for as long as it takes to make a wish. As before, they found themselves in front of the cave of the Master of the Seasons. Together they journeyed into the cave and into the warm light, and again they came face to face with the Master.

"Greta and Andy!" he exclaimed with some surprise. "You're back! I thought you wanted to leave summer. What brings you back now in the middle of winter?"

"Well," said Greta, "Andy and I are getting tired of winter. It's not fun anymore. Nobody does anything except sit around and talk and visit. Everybody always stays home and no one ever wants to go anywhere because it's too cold, or because it gets too dark too soon. So we came to ask you if you could begin spring. We'd be willing to help."

"The truth is," said the Master, "that spring and summer are very much like autumn and winter. Just as summer journeys through autumn and becomes winter, so now winter must journey through spring and become summer."

"See! I told you that's what he was going to tell us," cried Andy to Greta. "I knew that's the way it would be. And I bet there's a secret to it all, too; isn't there?" asked Andy, causing the Master simply to smile.

86

"Well, yes, there is, Andy," answered the Master. "And I'll be glad to share it with you if you wish. Would you like to know it?"

Both Greta and Andy grew excited, having completely forgotten about the times they had wished they had never known the secret of journeying from summer into winter. So they agreed, and together they sat with the Master of the Seasons in the center of the light that filled his cave.

"Like the first secret, this secret, too, has three conditions if you wish to journey into summer. First, you must again be willing to follow the wind, high so that your dreams can float free among the clouds and gentle so that even the most shy dream will not be fearful. Second, you must be willing to step out of the shadows and darkness and into the light — into the brightness where you can be known and seen clearly for what you are and what you do. And finally, you must be willing to step out from the warmth provided by those who are close to you; you must step out into what now seems cold, and trust that a new warmth will be given you, a warmth that comes as we are set free to make winter's new dreams come true. You will find warmth, but first you must trust and risk. Those are the terms, Greta and Andy. The secret is now yours. There is no turning back."

The Master of the Seasons then grew silent. His total treasure, the secret of winter and the secret of summer, he had now shared. The light in the cave slowly began to dim, and as it did so did the Master begin to fade from the light and into memory. Soon Greta and Andy stood alone in the gloomy, shadowed cave. The wind outside whistled the song of early spring, and a new sun seemed to spin a new brightness. Greta and Andy stepped out into the cold in search of the warmth that comes from making dreams come true. As they began home, Greta followed one path and Andy another, both to build castles in the clouds and to plant freedom in the hearts of new friends. Indeed, winter had begun the journey through spring and into summer.

In the weeks that followed, new life unraveled; and together the sun and the rain fairy-dusted the land with blossoms of gentle color. Each day more and more people stepped out into the brightness and warmth that enabled dreams to sprout forth. They planted their dreams in the clouds and watered them with their love. They danced on the wind and flirted with the sun. Spring had set the people free, spinning them into a summer of dreams come true.

Once, many seasons later, Greta and Andy made their way back to the cave where they had first come to know the Master of the Seasons and the secrets which he gave them. Together they stood there, alone with their memories and one with the secrets of life's rhythm. As they were about to leave, Greta bent down at the entrance to the cave to pick some splash of flowers. They were all that remained of a springtime rainbow which had once marked a promise to keep two secrets. As she lifted her head, her eye caught some words carved into the stone many seasons past. Andy saw them, too, and stooped low next to Greta. Together they whispered to one another the blessing they had found.

> *To all of his daughters and all of his sons,*
> *Two gifts of hope, God always brings.*
> *Carved out of love and shaped into seasons,*
> *One is roots, the other is wings.*

And in the end

The
Cherrytree

In the very same year Rosc*found both a son and a cherrytree planted in his life. Both were born with dreams of fruit the future would bring, and both were loved with tenderness. Both changed Rosc's life quite radically. While the cherrytree became the pride of his yard, his son became the pride of his family. In spring the cherrytree would be fertilized and in autumn meticulously pruned. Of all the trees about Rosc's home, none received care as did the cherrytree. And though Rosc had other children, this son he secretly loved the most. It was of great joy to him, therefore, that from the day of his son's birth, the two became known as old Rosc and young Rosc. To this day neither is known by any other name.

* pronounced Rosh

Old Rosc longed to see the fruit of his days, but the One who gives life was to have it differently. Before young Rosc was of the age to leave home, and before the cherrytree had grown sufficient to transform blossoms into red fruit, old Rosc died. Young Rosc helped make the coffin — of cherrywood; and thus the bond was sealed forever — young Rosc to the cherrytree, both to the love old Rosc had implanted deep within their spirits.

In the years that followed only young Rosc was aware how both he and the cherrytree reflected one another. As young Rosc grew older he fell in love and married. Together young Rosc and his beloved began a family — the same year that the cherrytree's white blossoms first bore fruit. Everyone marveled at the innocent beauty reflected in the infant, and later that year all the neighbors delighted in the rich, red cherries from the tree once planted by old Rosc. Never, they said, had a cherrytree been so rich in its first year of bearing fruit.

The following year young Rosc went to war. It was what every young man did who believed in his nation. In those years stolen by war the cherrytree bore no fruit. Strange, the neighbors would say, it's almost as if the spirits of the two were bound to one another.

Young Rosc returned from the war somehow changed — though it was difficult to say just how the war had reshaped him. Had the war stolen his love, wondered his family, or had it taught him to be cautious and preserve it lest it be squandered needlessly? In his own heart young Rosc had no doubt that he still loved his family. Though his love had grown quiet, it was not silent. His family grew and with it his love — a hidden love, certainly present and occasionally revealed in his smile or his gentleness or his need to be loved.

In the years that followed, little changed. Young Rosc continued to care for his family, and as his family grew, so did the cherrytree. Together the family lived in the home where young Rosc had been born, a home now cooled by the shade of the cherrytree grown tall and broad, never barren yet always bearing little fruit. In time the children moved from home to shape their own lives; and finally only young Rosc and the wife he had always loved remained — just the two of them, much as they had first begun.

One autumn, after almost sixty seasons of life had passed for both the cherrytree and young Rosc, his family began to wonder if perhaps the time had come to cut down the cherrytree. For too many seasons now the fruit had been sparse and the tree was growing old. On that day young Rosc's son left the family gathering saddened. He knew they were probably right. The cherrytree had grown old and never did bear much fruit, and in recent years the trunk had begun to crack and split open. With every wind storm young Rosc would wonder if the cherrytree would continue to shade the roof or if the roof would be claimed as a victim of the cherrytree's old age.

That Autumn day young Rosc's son climbed to the roof of their home and sat in the shade of the cherrytree's huge branches. There he whispered to the cherrytree of the words spoken within the home shortly before. Young Rosc's son sensed that the cherrytree understood, though what the outcome would be he was not sure. Why, he often wondered, had the cherrytree always borne so little fruit — particularly when its branches grew so high and full and lush with foliage. Someday he hoped to know. But for now, young Rosc's son was content to have shared with the cherrytree the secret of the family's conversation.

In the winter months that followed, young Rosc grew strangely weak. Eventually he went to the doctors and was told that he was seriously ill, that he would not recover, and worse that he would die shortly. While the doctors had told him it was a matter of weeks, or months at best, inwardly young Rosc decided he needed more time. Throughout his life, ever since the war, he was cautious with his expressions of love, fearful that his love was not sufficient to last a lifetime, and unsure of how to handle people's response. Now with little time remaining, young Rosc set about to share whatever love he yet had. He told his family of his great love for them, something he had seldom said with words in years past. Friendships took on new meaning, and with his love he carved gentle moments of time passed in remembering and rebuilding. He healed divisions with the peace love brings and dispelled fear with the hope he had discovered. Young Rosc survived the spring as well as the summer, and throughout those seasons he loved and was loved in ways never known by him or his family. Strangely, he discovered, his love did not grow stale or brittle nor was it consumed only to leave empty memories. Rather, his love bore much fruit — the blessing of his final days.

It was in that same summer that the cherrytree grew heavy with rich, ripe, red fruit. Never before had it been so fruitful — almost as if it had always borne fruit cautiously lest it should find itself barren, having squandered all early in life. Now was the time to be lavish. During those warm summer days young Rosc would wonder out loud who would pick the cherries, gently reminding his family that love shared needs a response. Always one of his children would climb the roof where the branches could easily be reached, and there they harvested the cherrytree's love. For both the cherrytree and young Rosc it became a summer richly blessed — a time of grace as no other time in their sixty years shared together.

Soon the autumn sky turned grey and cold, and winter once again nested in the land. When springtime returned, all was no longer the same. That spring there were no blossoms on the cherrytree, no buds for leaves, no new growth. And when young Rosc's family gathered for a family meal, one chair sat empty. Indeed, their lives had been changed. Yet in the days that followed, the entire neighborhood remembered young Rosc who loved his family as no other had and the cherrytree that once bore more fruit in one season than did other trees in a lifetime.

The
Sitting
Rock

The Sitting Rock

I truly wish that the story I am about to share with you were of my own making. It is not. I first came upon it in a tiny wisp of creation in western Wisconsin known as Durward's Glen. Since I first came to know the story, I have come upon others who also were told the same story, in the same place, and in the same way. So if it is your wish to verify its truth, all you need do is journey to the glen and listen with silence.

The glen was once owned by Bernard Durward, a poet, painter, and professor, as his tombstone perched on the crest of the glen attests. He lived in the latter years of the nineteenth century and apparently had acquired some local fame as a literateur. The glen affords an excellent opportunity for reflective escape which is no doubt why Bernard Durward chose to spend large portions of his life there.

96

The glen is a small, cool canyon buttressed among western Wisconsin's rolling hills. A clear, spring-fed creek bounces through the glen, playing hide-and-go-seek first with the sky, then with the sandstone walls of the glen, and then again with the sky. The predominent texture and mood of the canyoned glen is green, for nature has mossed the huge boulders, hung ferns from the sky, and provided a massive awning of trees. If one discovers the glen, one also wonders if it is ever possible to rediscover the outside world.

In the middle of the glen, on the eastern edge of the creek, there is a large flat sitting-rock about a foot above the surface of the creek. It cannot be missed, should you go seeking it, for it is the only sitting-rock there so close to the water. It was there that I heard this story. I sat there in silence, my legs crossed and my eyes sealed by arrows of sunlight shot through the leafy sky. For a long time only the creek spoke with gurgly sounds, laughing at a world she had just eluded. Then, mixed with the song of the creek, the story began.

I am the spirit of Durward's Glen — not a ghost, you must understand, but a spirit. Giorgi first came here in the youthful years of his manhood and sat on the rock where you now sit. He came with dreams in his heart. As he sat on the rock with his eyes closed and his ears atuned to the glen, the spirit of the glen nudged his heart and there whispered a promise — three wishes you may have for whatever it is you dream, one on this day, the second ten years from now to the day, and the third ten years following the second. The only condition is that you return on the day of the tenth year following each wish. Giorgi agreed and here on this rock made his first wish — sufficient wealth that he should never be in need.

Giorgi left the glen that day and within the week discovered he could purchase the glen and its surrounding woods and fields if he but agreed to settle and live there. This Giorgi did, building a small hut near the glen and a water wheel and mill adjacent to the creek. The top soil was rich, and the crops of grain bore a plentiful harvest. Settlers that followed also prospered on the land and brought their grain to Giorgi's mill. In the ten years that followed Giorgi's first visit to the glen he became the most prosperous of all the farmers in the area, both as a result of his own fields and as a result of the income from the mill.

Ten years to the day Giorgi returned to the sitting-rock along the eastern edge of the creek in the glen. As he had done ten years earlier, he closed his eyes and atuned his ears to the glen, and again the spirit of the glen nudged his heart and whispered the promise of three wishes. Giorgi expressed his delight that his first wish had been fulfilled and hesitatingly inquired if it were now possible to make the second of his three wishes. The spirit agreed and there, on that same sitting-rock, Giorgi wished for a family — a loving wife and healthy children with whom he might share his wealth.

Giorgi returned to his farmhouse and mill that day with new hope that his second wish might be fulfilled. Within that first year Giorgi met Marya. They fell in love, and before the year ended they exchanged vows. Soon children came, first a son, then two daughters, and by the end of the second decade a second son was born, enlarging Giorgi's family to six in number. All were healthy, and their beauty reflected the love of their dark skinned father and their gentle featured mother.

At the end of that second decade — to the day, Giorgi slipped back to the glen alone for he had never shared with his family the promise of the sitting-rock and the spirit's three wishes. For the third time in his life Giorgi came to the sitting-rock, closed his eyes, and atuned his ears to the whispers of the glen. For the third time the spirit of the glen nudged his heart and whispered the promise of the three wishes — this time with the gentle reminder that part of the bargain was to return at the end of each decade, even the last. To this Giorgi agreed readily, though he did not understand why it was necessary. The spirit only reminded him of the terms originally made twenty years previously and then inquired as to what Giorgi's third wish might be. To grow in wisdom among his fellows was Giorgi's third request. The spirit only smiled, as if to know the outcome and what would follow.

Giorgi returned, then, to his mill and fields and to the love of his family. In the decade that followed he grew more and more prosperous as more and more settlers came to farm the local area's rich earth. In this decade, too, a third son was born to him and Marya. But most noticeable of all was how Giorgi grew in wisdom and in respect among the local inhabitants. While he milled their grain, they would pour out their woes and their struggles. Always Giorgi would listen and in the end would offer suggestions for healing troubled marriages and mending neighborhood conflicts. By the end of the decade he was known throughout the region for his wisdom and sense of justice. The third wish had been granted. Yet Giorgi could not understand why it was necessary to return to the glen — unless, he wondered, it was because he had been so generous with what he had received that now the spirit of the glen would grant him a fourth wish. So taken up by this possibility was Giorgi that, even before the day of return had arrived, Giorgi had decided what the wish would be — one which could never be denied.

The day finally arrived and for the fourth time Giorgi returned to the glen. He walked straight to the sitting-rock, closed his eyes and atuned his ears to the whisper of the glen. The spirit of the glen was immediately present — as though it had arrived this time before Giorgi and was now found waiting. Giorgi immediately took the initiative and told how he did not understand the necessity of his returning a fourth time and how he had begun to wonder if it might not be possible for him to be granted a fourth wish — since the spirit and he were there together anyway. The spirit of the glen quickly protested, but Glorgi persisted and finally proclaimed that his fourth wish was to become holy. Could it be granted?

With that request, the sounds of the glen abruptly stilled. For a moment all motion ceased, all except for the spirit who quietly smiled as if it had been playing out a script written three decades earlier, only to find it all now come true. Very well, agreed the spirit of the glen. Since that is your request, be it so. It is now granted. Giorgi left the glen that day thinking he had won the world and salvation too.

That summer a drought began in western Wisconsin. Giorgi's fields as well as the fields of all those in the area lay barren and scorched. Harvests of grain were minimal as was also the work in the mill as a result. The following summer was no different. The entire area suffered now; even Giorgi and his family began to feel the oppression. The winter that year came early and was severe. It was during that winter that Giorgi's and Marya's youngest son began to fail in health. None of the doctors knew why, and before the spring thaw, their youngest had died and been buried. The following summer and the three that succeeded completed the six year drought — one of the most dreadful in Wisconsin's history. With barren fields and a dried up creek, the mill grew rusty and fell into disrepair. No longer did the local residents come; no longer was Giorgi recognized as one with wisdom. All had forgotten. During the fifth summer of the drought, both of his daughters fell in love and married. When the drought persisted for the sixth summer both daughters and their husbands and new borns, grandchildren for Giorgi and Marya, moved to the growing cities near Lake Michigan in search of industrial work. Their moves caused Giorgi and Marya great pain, for now only two sons remained at home — and how long that could continue was doubtful. After the drought, Giorgi was never able to recoup his financial losses. Marya was growing more and more arthritic and as a result more and more house-bound. It was after such a course of events that Giorgi was forced to sell the glen (some say to Bernard Durward) in order to find some comfort in the final days for himself and Marya. To Giorgi it all seemed a most strange and painful decade to follow upon a wish for holiness. Perhaps he had presumed too much in requesting a fourth wish. Had he not been free of all anxiety and strangely at peace, it would have seemed to him almost a punishment.

The date on the bill of sale for the glen was exactly forty years to the day after Giorgi had first come upon the sitting-rock and the spirit of the glen that had promised three wishes. Having signed the bill of sale, Giorgi made one final journey to the sitting-rock. He came and closed his eyes and atuned his ears to the glen, waiting for the spirit of the glen to nudge his heart. The spirit did come and both sat in silence. Finally Giorgi asked why the fourth wish had not been fulfilled. Had he been too bold in requesting it? Had he failed in some way to be faithful? Why had he not grown holy?

To the contrary, the spirit began, the wish had been granted and fulfilled. To be holy, one must empty oneself of all of that to which one clings in life — of wealth, of knowledge and power, yes even of possessing those who are the closest. Once one has emptied oneself of all that fills life, only then is there room for God, for even God cannot fill what is already full. Giorgi had begun the process of growing holy.

Thus the story ended. My eyes opened and I looked about. Nothing in the glen had changed — only I. The spirit of the glen had moved on; now only God's spirit remained, waiting to fill a life that first needed to be emptied.